THE BUMPER BOOK OF BUNNY SUICIDES

EITHER

OR

VALEAS MUNDUM

ANDY RILEY IS THE AUTHOR/ARTIST OF THE BOOK OF BUNNY SUICIDES, RETURN OF THE BUNNY SUICIDES, GREAT LIES To Tell Small Kids AND LOADS MORE LIES TO TELL SMALL KIDS. HE DRAWS ROASTED, A WEEKLY COMIC STRIP IN THE OBSERVER MAGAZINE. HE IS THE CO-CREATOR OF BBC2's HYPERDRIVE, RADIO FOUR'S THE 99p CHALLENGE AND SLACKER CATS, A NEW ANIMATED SITCOM FOR AMERICAN TV. HE HAS ALSO WRITTEN FOR BLACK BOOKS, LITTLE BRITAIN, THE ARMANDO IANNUCCI SHOWS, SMACK THE PONY, BIG TRAIN, THE ARMSTRONG AND MILLER SHOW, SPITTING IMAGE, THE FRIDAY NIGHT ARMISTICE, So GRAHAM NORTON, ALEXI SAYLE'S MERRY GO ROUND AND THE BAFTA-WINNING ROBBIE THE REINDEER. AND HIM AND KEVIN GOT FOUR JOKES INTO TIM BURTON'S THE CORPSE BRIDE.

THE BUMPER BOOK OF BUNNY SUICIDES

ANDY RILEY

H

HODDER &
STOUGHTON

FIRST PUBLISHED IN GREAT BRITAIN IN 2003 AND 2004 BY HODDER AND STOUGHTON
A DIVISION OF HODDER HEADLINE

A HODDER PAPERBACK BOOK
1

A CIP CATALOGUE RECORD FOR THIS TITLE IS AVAILABLE FROM THE BRITISH LIBRARY.
ISBN 978 0 340 92370 2

PRINTED AND BOUND IN AUSTRALIA BY GRIFFIN PRESS
HODDER AND STOUGHTON
A DIVISION OF HODDER HEADLINE, 338 EUSTON ROAD, LONDON, NW1 3BH

WITH THANKS TO

KEVIN CECIL, ARTHUR MATHEWS, POLLY FABER,
CAMILLA HORNBY, NICK DAVIES AND ALL AT
HODDER & STOUGHTON, KATY FOLLAIN,
FREYA AYRES, DAVID AYRES.

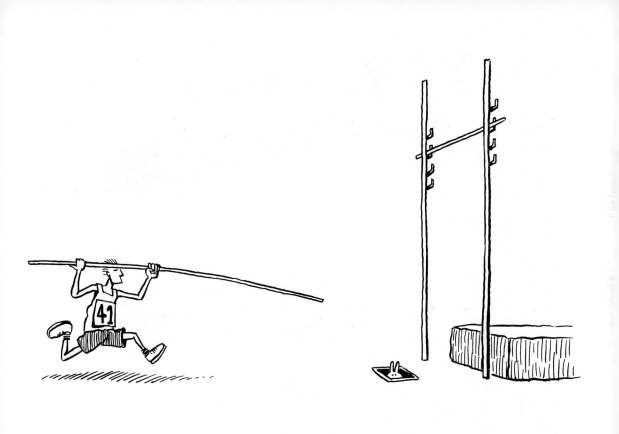

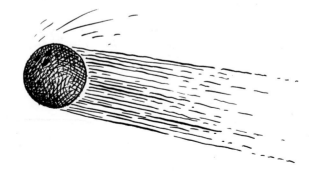

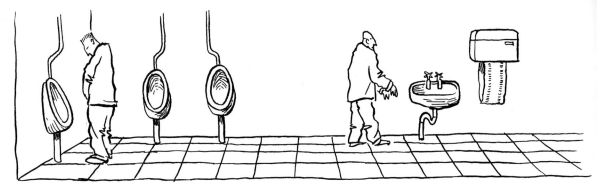

DANGER
LAND SPEED
RECORD
ATTEMPT
LEAVE AREA

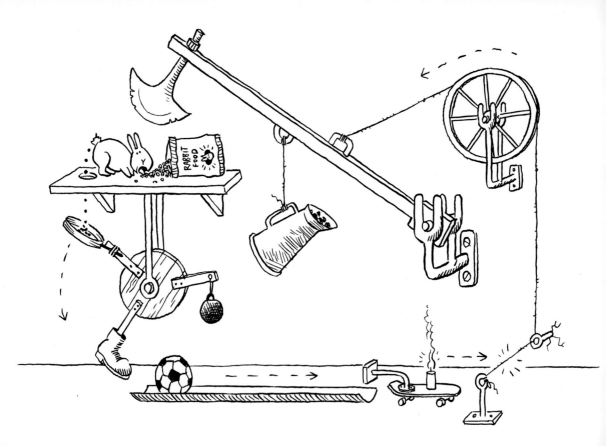

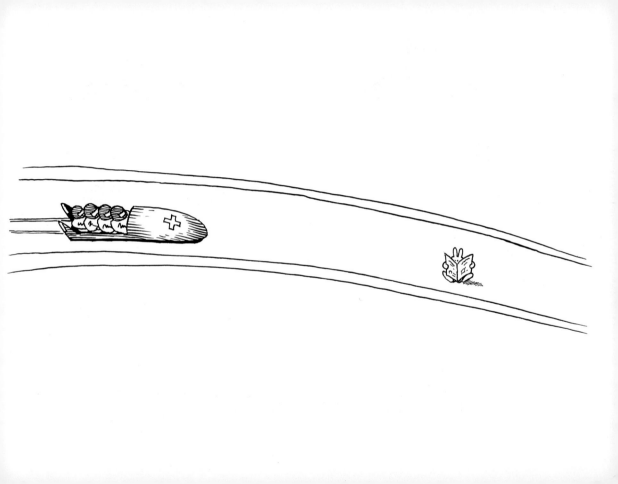

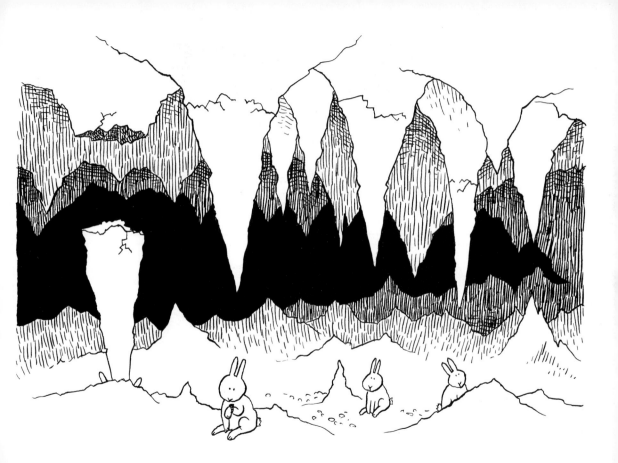

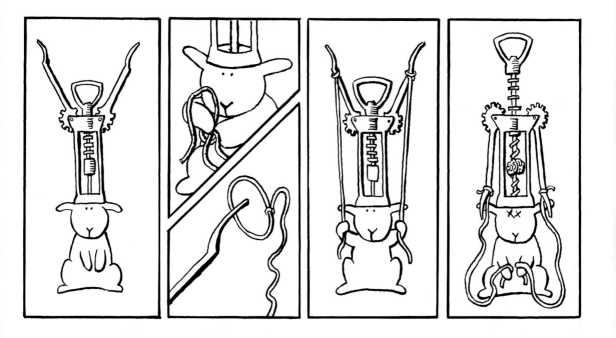

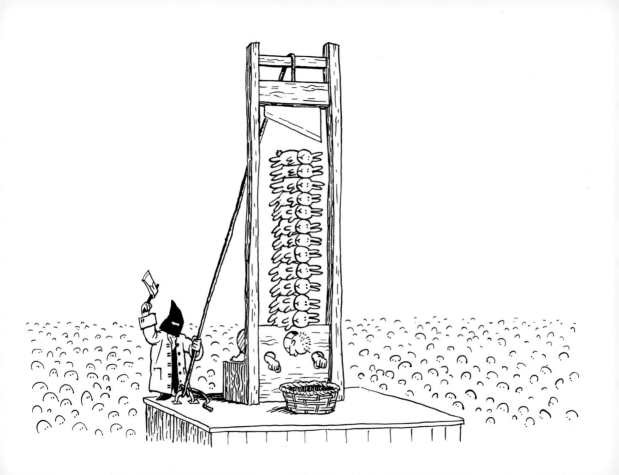

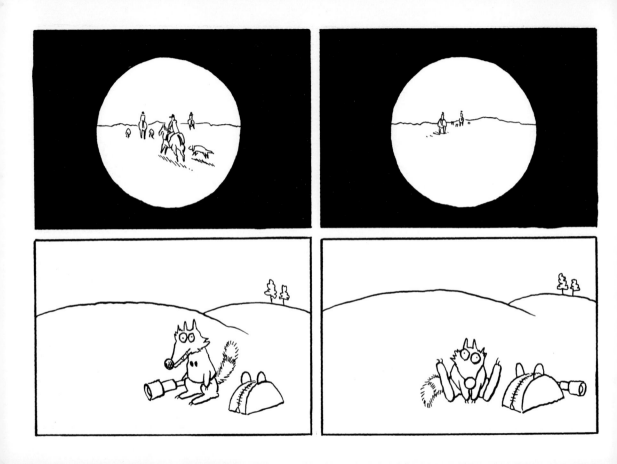

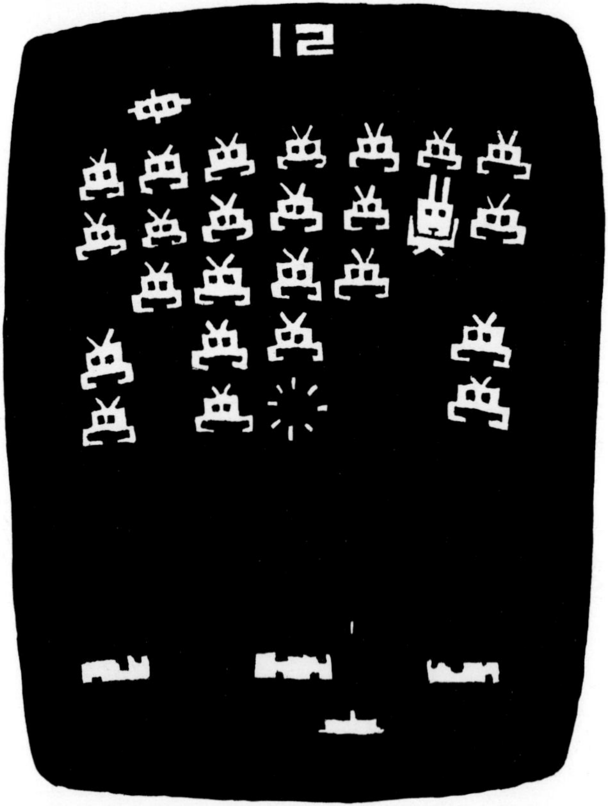
12

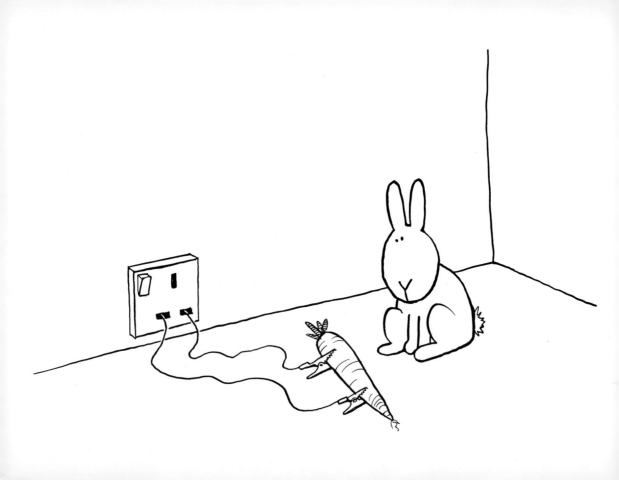

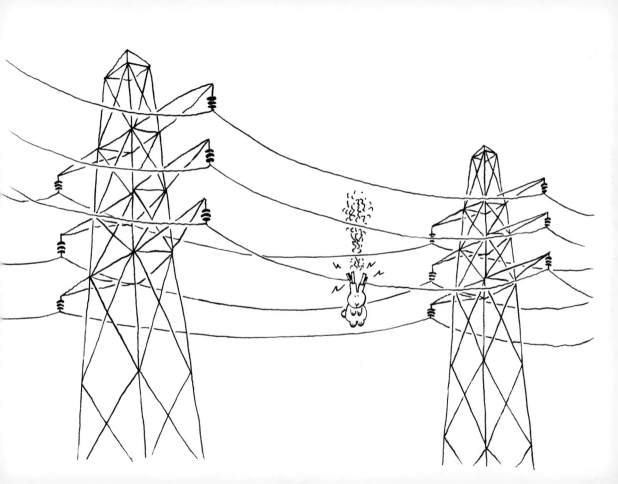

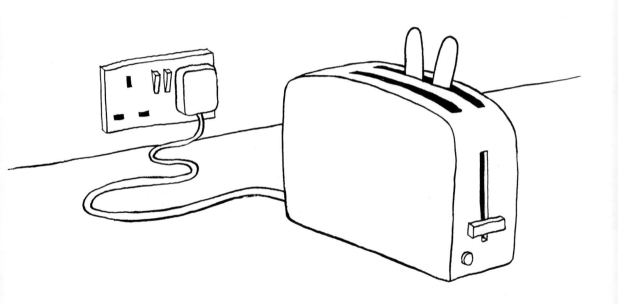

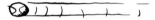

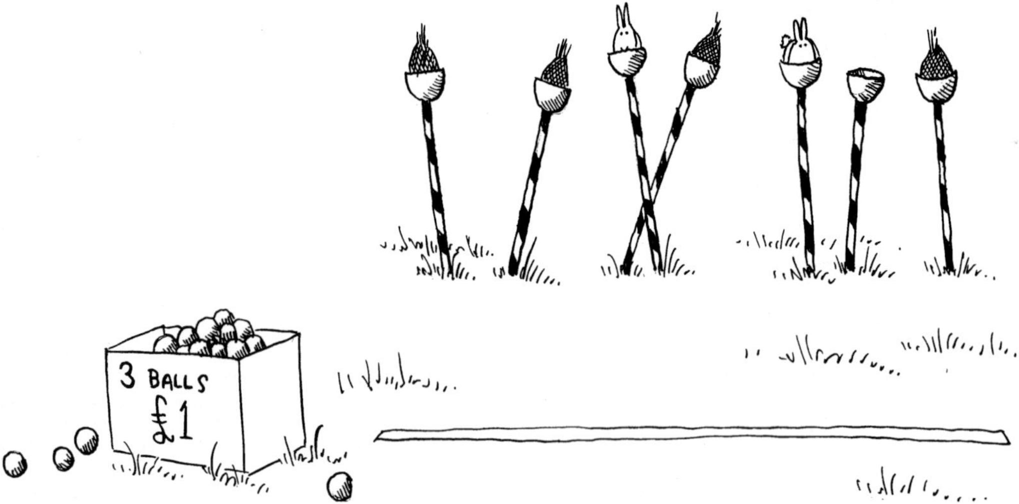
3 BALLS
£1

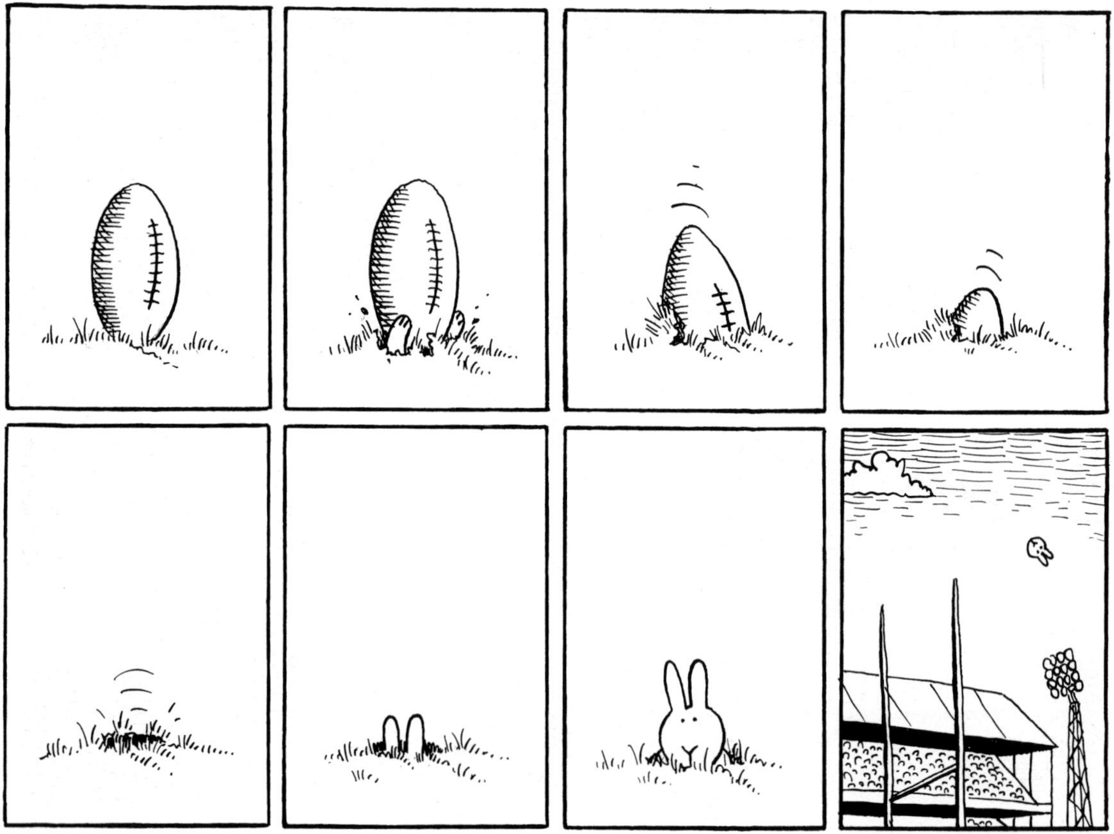

* TWO RABBITS JUGGLING CHISELS DURING A TOTAL ECLIPSE OF THE SUN

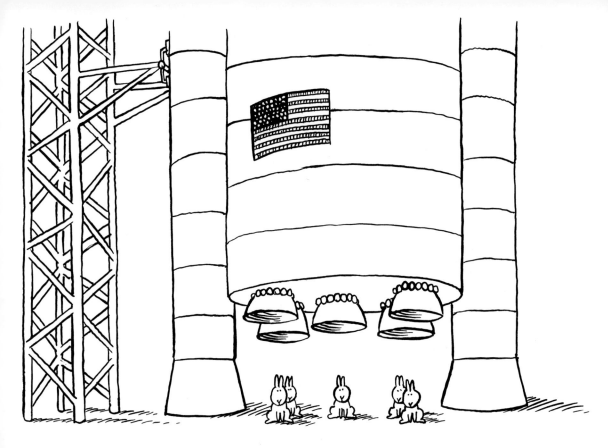

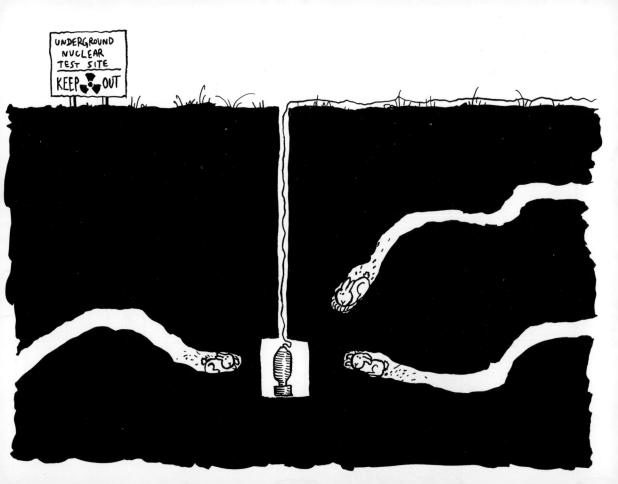

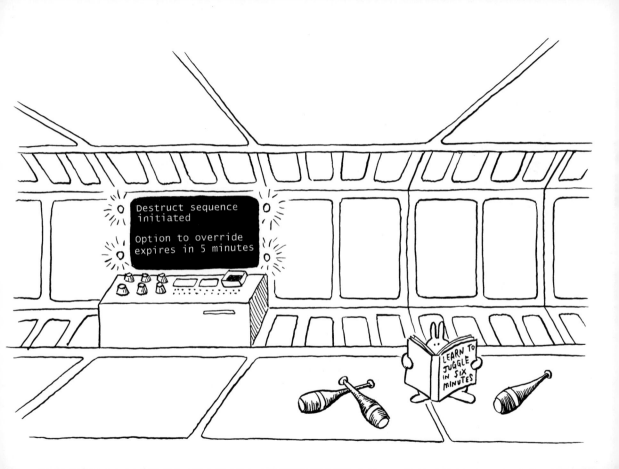

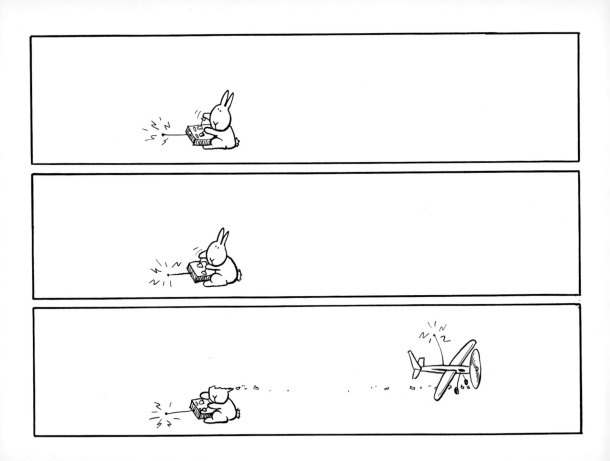

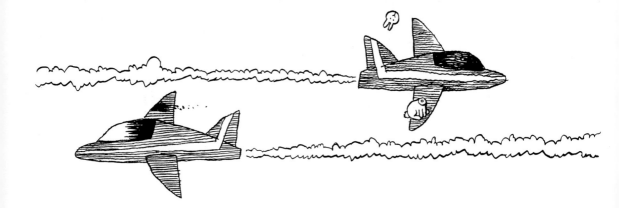

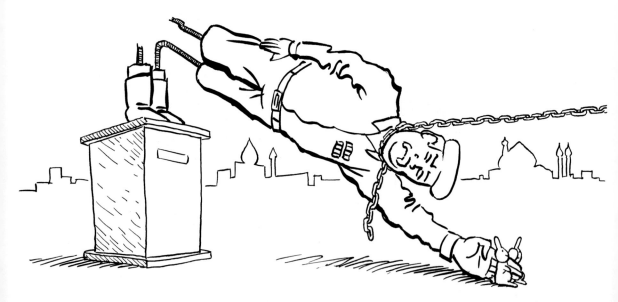

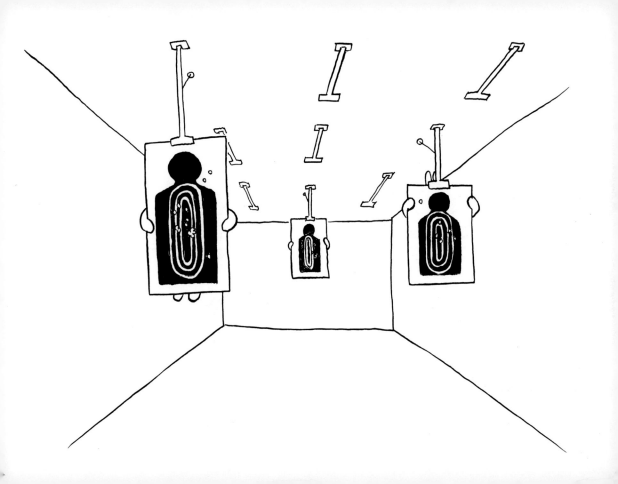

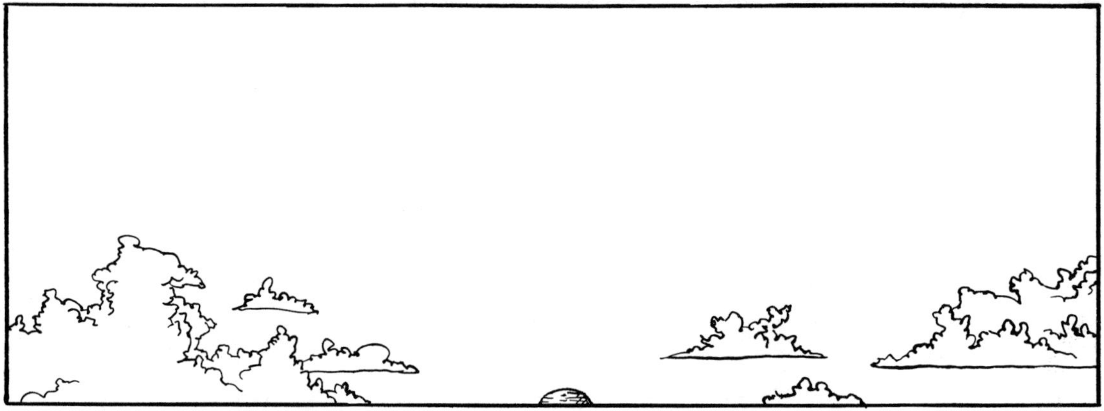
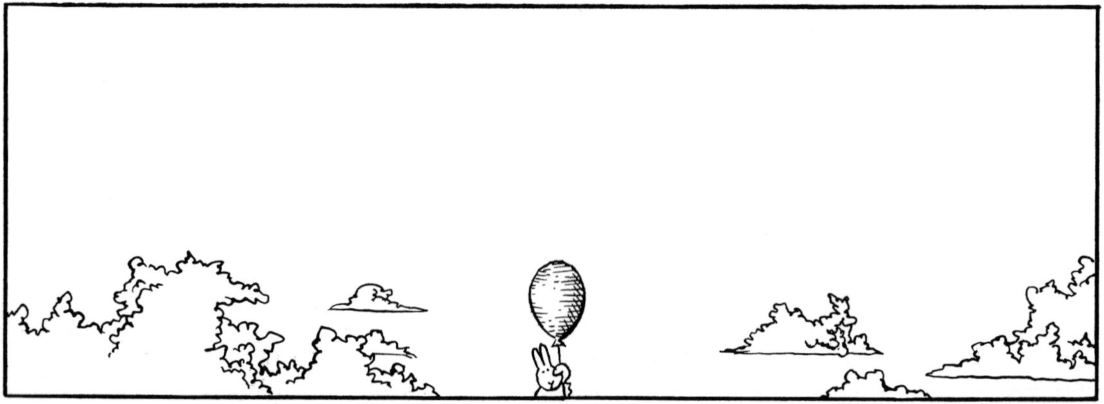

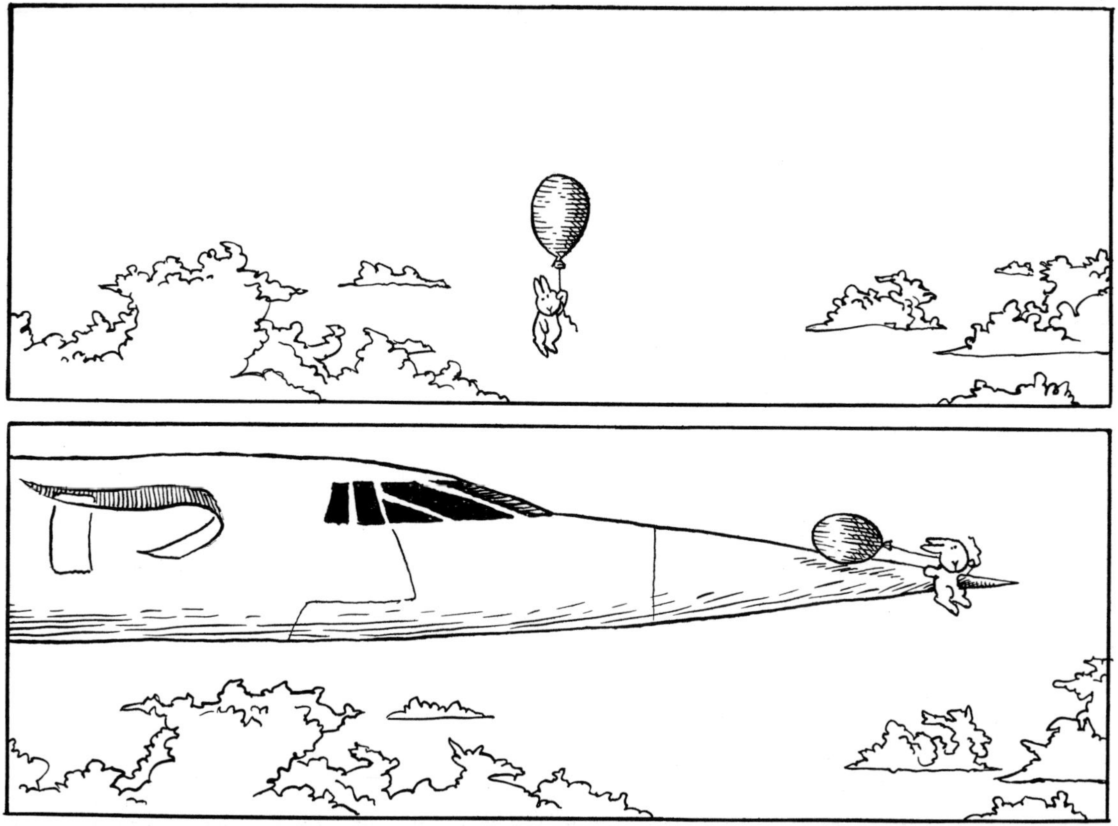

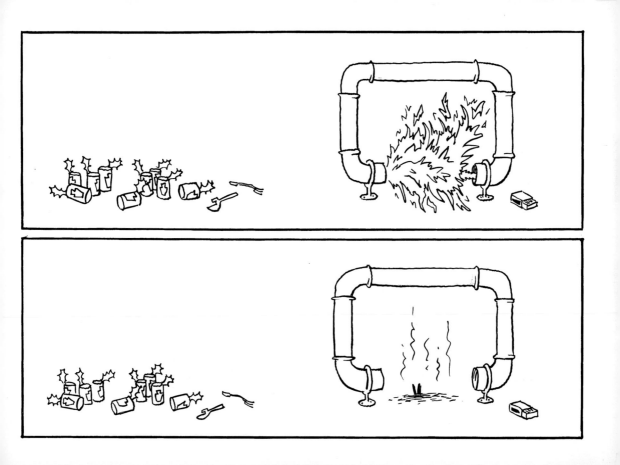